ONE ON ONE

MEETING
PLANNER

What is an One on One meeting?

A regular meeting between the manager and the employee, focusing on the conversation about the work, successes, challenges and development expectations of the latter.

The frequency should be flexible and adjusted to the current needs and situation. They can be held once a week, once a month or once a quarter.

It's often considered the most important meeting you can have because it lays the foundation for a trusting and productive work relationship.

Remember that One On One meetings should mainly be focused on the employee. If you take this opportunity to report a status of a project, evaluate the employee or use this time for reporting your employee will be discouraged from meetings and you will not receive the desired benefits.

Benefits of One on One Meetings

Relationship building

Regular One on One meetings primarily provide an opportunity to build a deeper relationship between a manager and an employee. This is a great time to get to know your team members better, their interests, and any short- and long-term challenges they face outside of work.

Feedback opportunity

How often do you ask your team members for feedback on your work? You can use One on One meetings to learn more about the way you lead your team. Aim to always ask your employees how you can support them in their daily jobs, challenges and projects.

Opportunity for every team member to voice their opinion

You probably know from experience that some voices are louder in group meetings. Not everyone has the opportunity to express their opinion and more shy people may not be willing to speak on the forum.

Learn about development goals of your team members

One on One meetings provide an opportunity to discuss the employee's professional aspirations and discuss their possible career paths.
You should reflect on this together:

- What skills (classes, certificates, experience) do the employee need?
- What tasks and projects may be valuable in supporting employee development?
- What are the most valuable talents and skills of an employee?

One on One meeting structure

When your meetings are held ona regular basis you may start wondering what topics to discuss to avoid boredom and repettiveness.

 The topics to be discussed can vary and should always be tailored to your needs.

Start with below staple topics & guidelines then expand into areas of your current needs or interests.

Key successes and challenges.

Upcoming projects.

Development goals and career plans.

The way you can support the employee in his work.

A chat about life, hobbies, family.

It is critical to always take notes!
Write down everything you consider important. Certainly, you will agree on more than once the next steps that you will want to take on a given topic. Without your notes, it will be hard to come back to them at the beginning of the next meeting. Remember to always review your notes before the meeting.

Types of One on One Meetings and top 5 questions to ask

First One on One with a new team member
- Tell me about yourself – what attracted you to this role?
- What are your aspirations – professionally and personally?
- What gives you energy, and what drains it?
- What's your role and what do you expect from me?
- Introduce your team and tell me how I can support you in their development.
- What do you recommend with regards to our communication and way of working.
- Anything else you'd like to talk about today?

Goal-setting meeting
- Let's talk about the set objectives and progress.
- How did previous objectives go?
- What are your priorities for the upcoming month?
- What are your current objectives and personal development goals.
- Your recommendations with regards to next steps.

Performance review debrief
- How do you feel after this performance review?
- What did you think about me previous feedback?
- Can I clarify anything for you?
- Were you surprised with anything?
- What's your main takeaway from this review?
- Any feedback regarding the way I communicated my feedback?

Performance improvement meeting

- Are you clear on what is expected of you? Do you think those expectations are realistic?
- Do you realize how your role fits into the bigger picture/why your work is important?
- Do you receive enough feedback? If not, why do you think you don't receive it? How could we ensure you get more feedback?
- Do you feel comfortable asking for support when needed?
- What got in the way of you having more impact? (e.g. internal processes, time management issues, lack of resources or information)
- What are action items and/or objectives we can agree on?

Regular check-in

- How did the past week/month go?How are you doing/feeling?
- What is on your agenda for today?
- What recent achievements are you proud of? Anything blocking you?
- Do you need any support? Is there anything I can do to support you?
- Anything else you'd like to talk about today?

Skip Level meeting

- What are you proud of?
- What ideas do you have for your team and the company?
- How do you feel about the vision and priorities of our company?
- What can your manager do better to support you in your role?
- Is anything blocking you?

Personal development conversation

- Based on the feedback you received lately, are there areas you would like to develop further?
- What next steps could you be taking towards those goals?
- What part of your job are you enjoying the most? What's inspiring, motivating, and energizing?
- What part of your job are you enjoying the least? What is frustrating or boring you? What is the one task you would love to stop doing if it was possible?
- Where do you see yourself in 2 years?

One on One meeting tips

1. Length of the meeting

It is said that a 1:1 meeting should last an hour, but it's really up to you. It could be an hour, 30 minutes, or even less. Let it last as long as necessary to cover all the important topics.

2. The invitation

As a manager, it is on your side to organize the meeting and send an invitation to the employee. If possible, leave yourself 15 minutes off before the next meeting in case your interview becomes prolonged.

3. When you need to cancel or postpone your meeting

Even if you get something up and you can't attend a scheduled meeting, don't cancel it. This is a very important rule. Consider shortening the meeting or holding it over the phone, and in the worst case, postpone it to another day. When you frequently cancel 1:1, you send a message to the employee that he and his affairs are irrelevant to you.

4. Frequency

I have already written that the frequency of meetings depends on individual needs. You can organize meetings once a week, twice a month or once a quarter. The key is to schedule them at regular intervals, preferably as a recurring event on your calendars.

5. Location

Not always 1:1 has to take place in the company's conference room. If possible, take an employee for a coffee at a nearby cafe.

6. Mindfulness

Remember to silence your phone, close your laptop and focus on your conversation. If you're having an online conversation, you'd better close all browser windows and mute Slack. Let me repeat myself here - it's time for you.

7. Agenda

To make meetings more effective, prepare an agenda in advance. Treat it as a kind of checklist, making sure that all the most important points of the meeting are discussed (an example agenda can be found further in the article). Of course, there are situations where we throw the agenda out of the window and have a long, casual conversation, but in most cases the agenda definitely helps.

8. Communication

If you speak more than you listen in a meeting, you are doing it wrong. Try to establish an environment where the employee speaks at least 70% of the time. Practice asking questions instead of telling people what you think

9. Atmosphere

1:1 meetings should definitely be informal. This is not the time for hierarchy and reporting. Additionally, create an atmosphere of mutual respect and trust. I am sure it will benefit both sides.

Meeting Index

Name of Participant (s)

Meeting Index

Meeting with

Date

1-2-1 type

- ☐ Regular check-in
- ☐ First 1:1 with a new team member
- ☐ Goal-setting meeting
- ☐ Performance review debrief
- ☐ Performance improvement meeting
- ☐ Skip-level meeting template
- ☐ Growth conversation

Agenda
(list of topics)

Meeting discusion notes

Observations / Concerns

Action Items

Follow up meeting plan

Notes

Meeting with	Date	1-2-1 type

Meeting with

....

....

Date

1-2-1 type

☐ Regular check-in

☐ First 1:1 with a new team member

☐ Goal-setting meeting

☐ Performance review debrief

☐ Performance improvement meeting

☐ Skip-level meeting template

☐ Growth conversation

Agenda
(list of topics)

....

....

....

....

....

Meeting discusion notes

Observations / Concerns

Action Items

Follow up meeting plan

Notes

Meeting with

....
....

Date

1-2-1 type

- [ ] Regular check-in
- [ ] First 1:1 with a new team member
- [ ] Goal-setting meeting
- [ ] Performance review debrief
- [ ] Performance improvement meeting
- [ ] Skip-level meeting template
- [ ] Growth conversation

Agenda
(list of topics)

....
....
....
....
....

Meeting discusion notes

Observations / Concerns

Action Items

Follow up meeting plan

Notes

Meeting with

Date

1-2-1 type

☐ Regular check-in

☐ First 1:1 with a new team member

☐ Goal-setting meeting

☐ Performance review debrief

☐ Performance improvement meeting

☐ Skip-level meeting template

☐ Growth conversation

Agenda
(list of topics)

Meeting discusion notes

18

Observations / Concerns

Action Items

Follow up meeting plan

Notes

Meeting with

....
....

Date

1-2-1 type

- ☐ Regular check-in
- ☐ First 1:1 with a new team member
- ☐ Goal-setting meeting
- ☐ Performance review debrief
- ☐ Performance improvement meeting
- ☐ Skip-level meeting template
- ☐ Growth conversation

Agenda
(list of topics)

....
....
....
....
....

Meeting discusion notes

Observations / Concerns

Action Items

Follow up meeting plan

Notes

Meeting with

Date

1-2-1 type

☐ Regular check-in

☐ First 1:1 with a new team member

☐ Goal-setting meeting

☐ Performance review debrief

☐ Performance improvement meeting

☐ Skip-level meeting template

☐ Growth conversation

Agenda
(list of topics)

Meeting discusion notes

Observations / Concerns

Action Items

Follow up meeting plan

Notes

Meeting with

Date

1-2-1 type

☐ Regular check-in

☐ First 1:1 with a new team member

☐ Goal-setting meeting

☐ Performance review debrief

☐ Performance improvement meeting

☐ Skip-level meeting template

☐ Growth conversation

Agenda
(list of topics)

Meeting discusion notes

Observations / Concerns

Action Items

Follow up meeting plan

Notes

Meeting with

Date

1-2-1 type

☐ Regular check-in

☐ First 1:1 with a new team member

☐ Goal-setting meeting

☐ Performance review debrief

☐ Performance improvement meeting

☐ Skip-level meeting template

☐ Growth conversation

Agenda
(list of topics)

Meeting discusion notes

Observations / Concerns

Action Items

Follow up meeting plan

Notes

Meeting with

....
....

Date

1-2-1 type

- [ ] Regular check-in
- [ ] First 1:1 with a new team member
- [ ] Goal-setting meeting
- [ ] Performance review debrief
- [ ] Performance improvement meeting
- [ ] Skip-level meeting template
- [ ] Growth conversation

Agenda
(list of topics)

....
....
....
....
....

Meeting discusion notes

Observations / Concerns

Action Items

Follow up meeting plan

Notes

Meeting with

Date

1-2-1 type

☐ Regular check-in

☐ First 1:1 with a new team member

☐ Goal-setting meeting

☐ Performance review debrief

☐ Performance improvement meeting

☐ Skip-level meeting template

☐ Growth conversation

Agenda
(list of topics)

Meeting discusion notes

Observations / Concerns

Action Items

Follow up meeting plan

Notes

Meeting with

Date

1-2-1 type

- [ ] Regular check-in
- [ ] First 1:1 with a new team member
- [ ] Goal-setting meeting
- [ ] Performance review debrief
- [ ] Performance improvement meeting
- [ ] Skip-level meeting template
- [ ] Growth conversation

Agenda
(list of topics)

Meeting discusion notes

Observations / Concerns

Action Items

Follow up meeting plan

Notes

Meeting with

Date

1-2-1 type

- [ ] Regular check-in
- [ ] First 1:1 with a new team member
- [ ] Goal-setting meeting
- [ ] Performance review debrief
- [ ] Performance improvement meeting
- [ ] Skip-level meeting template
- [ ] Growth conversation

Agenda
(list of topics)

Meeting discusion notes

Observations / Concerns

Action Items

Follow up meeting plan

Notes

Meeting with

Date

1-2-1 type

☐ Regular check-in

☐ First 1:1 with a new team member

☐ Goal-setting meeting

☐ Performance review debrief

☐ Performance improvement meeting

☐ Skip-level meeting template

☐ Growth conversation

Agenda
(list of topics)

Meeting discusion notes

Observations / Concerns

Action Items

Follow up meeting plan

Notes

Meeting with

Date

1-2-1 type

- [ ] Regular check-in
- [ ] First 1:1 with a new team member
- [ ] Goal-setting meeting
- [ ] Performance review debrief
- [ ] Performance improvement meeting
- [ ] Skip-level meeting template
- [ ] Growth conversation

Agenda
(list of topics)

Meeting discusion notes

Observations / Concerns

Action Items

Follow up meeting plan

Notes

Meeting with

Date

1-2-1 type

- [ ] Regular check-in
- [ ] First 1:1 with a new team member
- [ ] Goal-setting meeting
- [ ] Performance review debrief
- [ ] Performance improvement meeting
- [ ] Skip-level meeting template
- [ ] Growth conversation

Agenda
(list of topics)

Meeting discusion notes

Observations / Concerns

Action Items

Follow up meeting plan

Notes

Meeting with

Date

1-2-1 type

☐ Regular check-in

☐ First 1:1 with a new team member

☐ Goal-setting meeting

☐ Performance review debrief

☐ Performance improvement meeting

☐ Skip-level meeting template

☐ Growth conversation

Agenda
(list of topics)

Meeting discusion notes

Observations / Concerns

Action Items

Follow up meeting plan

Notes

Meeting with

Date

1-2-1 type

- ☐ Regular check-in
- ☐ First 1:1 with a new team member
- ☐ Goal-setting meeting
- ☐ Performance review debrief
- ☐ Performance improvement meeting
- ☐ Skip-level meeting template
- ☐ Growth conversation

Agenda
(list of topics)

Meeting discusion notes

Observations / Concerns

Action Items

Follow up meeting plan

Notes

Meeting with

....

....

Date

1-2-1 type

- [ ] Regular check-in
- [ ] First 1:1 with a new team member
- [ ] Goal-setting meeting
- [ ] Performance review debrief
- [ ] Performance improvement meeting
- [ ] Skip-level meeting template
- [ ] Growth conversation

Agenda
(list of topics)

....

....

....

....

....

Meeting discusion notes

Observations / Concerns

Action Items

Follow up meeting plan

Notes

Meeting with

....

....

Date

1-2-1 type

☐ Regular check-in

☐ First 1:1 with a new team member

☐ Goal-setting meeting

☐ Performance review debrief

☐ Performance improvement meeting

☐ Skip-level meeting template

☐ Growth conversation

Agenda
(list of topics)

....

....

....

....

....

Meeting discusion notes

Observations / Concerns

Action Items

Follow up meeting plan

Notes

Meeting with

Date

1-2-1 type
- ☐ Regular check-in
- ☐ First 1:1 with a new team member
- ☐ Goal-setting meeting
- ☐ Performance review debrief
- ☐ Performance improvement meeting
- ☐ Skip-level meeting template
- ☐ Growth conversation

Agenda
(list of topics)

Meeting discusion notes

Observations / Concerns

Action Items

Follow up meeting plan

Notes

Meeting with

Date

☐ Regular check-in

☐ First 1:1 with a new team member

☐ Goal-setting meeting

☐ Performance review debrief

☐ Performance improvement meeting

☐ Skip-level meeting template

☐ Growth conversation

Agenda
(list of topics)

Meeting discusion notes

Observations / Concerns

Action Items

Follow up meeting plan

Notes

Meeting with

Date

1-2-1 type

☐ Regular check-in

☐ First 1:1 with a new team member

☐ Goal-setting meeting

☐ Performance review debrief

☐ Performance improvement meeting

☐ Skip-level meeting template

☐ Growth conversation

Agenda
(list of topics)

Meeting discusion notes

Observations / Concerns

Action Items

Follow up meeting plan

Notes

Meeting with

Date

1-2-1 type

☐ Regular check-in

☐ First 1:1 with a new team member

☐ Goal-setting meeting

☐ Performance review debrief

☐ Performance improvement meeting

☐ Skip-level meeting template

☐ Growth conversation

Agenda
(list of topics)

Meeting discusion notes

Observations / Concerns

Action Items

Follow up meeting plan

Notes

Meeting with

....
....

Date

1-2-1 type

- [ ] Regular check-in
- [ ] First 1:1 with a new team member
- [ ] Goal-setting meeting
- [ ] Performance review debrief
- [ ] Performance improvement meeting
- [ ] Skip-level meeting template
- [ ] Growth conversation

Agenda
(list of topics)

....
....
....
....
....

Meeting discusion notes

Observations / Concerns

Action Items

Follow up meeting plan

Notes

Meeting with

....

....

Date

1-2-1 type

☐ Regular check-in

☐ First 1:1 with a new team member

☐ Goal-setting meeting

☐ Performance review debrief

☐ Performance improvement meeting

☐ Skip-level meeting template

☐ Growth conversation

Agenda
(list of topics)

....

....

....

....

....

Meeting discusion notes

Observations / Concerns

Action Items

Follow up meeting plan

Notes

Meeting with
....
....

Date

1-2-1 type

☐ Regular check-in

☐ First 1:1 with a new team member

☐ Goal-setting meeting

☐ Performance review debrief

☐ Performance improvement meeting

☐ Skip-level meeting template

☐ Growth conversation

Agenda
(list of topics)
....
....
....
....
....

Meeting discusion notes

Observations / Concerns

Action Items

Follow up meeting plan

Notes

Meeting with

Date

1-2-1 type

- ☐ Regular check-in
- ☐ First 1:1 with a new team member
- ☐ Goal-setting meeting
- ☐ Performance review debrief
- ☐ Performance improvement meeting
- ☐ Skip-level meeting template
- ☐ Growth conversation

Agenda
(list of topics)

Meeting discusion notes

Observations / Concerns

Action Items

Follow up meeting plan

Notes

Meeting with

Date

1-2-1 type

☐ Regular check-in

☐ First 1:1 with a new team member

☐ Goal-setting meeting

☐ Performance review debrief

☐ Performance improvement meeting

☐ Skip-level meeting template

☐ Growth conversation

Agenda
(list of topics)

Meeting discusion notes

Observations / Concerns

Action Items

Follow up meeting plan

Notes

Meeting with

Date

1-2-1 type

☐ Regular check-in

☐ First 1:1 with a new team member

☐ Goal-setting meeting

☐ Performance review debrief

☐ Performance improvement meeting

☐ Skip-level meeting template

☐ Growth conversation

Agenda
(list of topics)

Meeting discusion notes

Observations / Concerns

Action Items

Follow up meeting plan

Notes

Meeting with

Date

1-2-1 type

- [ ] Regular check-in
- [ ] First 1:1 with a new team member
- [ ] Goal-setting meeting
- [ ] Performance review debrief
- [ ] Performance improvement meeting
- [ ] Skip-level meeting template
- [ ] Growth conversation

Agenda
(list of topics)

Meeting discusion notes

Observations / Concerns

Action Items

Follow up meeting plan

Notes

Meeting with

Date

1-2-1 type

☐ Regular check-in

☐ First 1:1 with a new team member

☐ Goal-setting meeting

☐ Performance review debrief

☐ Performance improvement meeting

☐ Skip-level meeting template

☐ Growth conversation

Agenda
(list of topics)

Meeting discusion notes

72

Observations / Concerns

Action Items

Follow up meeting plan

Notes

Meeting with

Date

1-2-1 type
- [ ] Regular check-in
- [ ] First 1:1 with a new team member
- [ ] Goal-setting meeting
- [ ] Performance review debrief
- [ ] Performance improvement meeting
- [ ] Skip-level meeting template
- [ ] Growth conversation

Agenda
(list of topics)

Meeting discusion notes

Observations / Concerns

Action Items

Follow up meeting plan

Notes

Meeting with

Date

1-2-1 type

☐ Regular check-in

☐ First 1:1 with a new team member

☐ Goal-setting meeting

☐ Performance review debrief

☐ Performance improvement meeting

☐ Skip-level meeting template

☐ Growth conversation

Agenda
(list of topics)

Meeting discusion notes

Observations / Concerns

Action Items

Follow up meeting plan

Notes

Meeting with

Date

- ☐ Regular check-in
- ☐ First 1:1 with a new team member
- ☐ Goal-setting meeting
- ☐ Performance review debrief
- ☐ Performance improvement meeting
- ☐ Skip-level meeting template
- ☐ Growth conversation

Agenda
(list of topics)

Meeting discusion notes

Observations / Concerns

Action Items

Follow up meeting plan

Notes

Meeting with

Date

1-2-1 type

- [ ] Regular check-in
- [ ] First 1:1 with a new team member
- [ ] Goal-setting meeting
- [ ] Performance review debrief
- [ ] Performance improvement meeting
- [ ] Skip-level meeting template
- [ ] Growth conversation

Agenda
(list of topics)

Meeting discusion notes

Observations / Concerns

Action Items

Follow up meeting plan

Notes

Meeting with
....
....

Date

1-2-1 type

☐ Regular check-in

☐ First 1:1 with a new team member

☐ Goal-setting meeting

☐ Performance review debrief

☐ Performance improvement meeting

☐ Skip-level meeting template

☐ Growth conversation

Agenda
(list of topics)

Meeting discusion notes

Observations / Concerns

Action Items

Follow up meeting plan

Notes

Meeting with

Date

1-2-1 type

- [ ] Regular check-in
- [ ] First 1:1 with a new team member
- [ ] Goal-setting meeting
- [ ] Performance review debrief
- [ ] Performance improvement meeting
- [ ] Skip-level meeting template
- [ ] Growth conversation

Agenda
(list of topics)

Meeting discusion notes

Observations / Concerns

Action Items

Follow up meeting plan

Notes

Meeting with
....
....

Date

1-2-1 type

☐ Regular check-in

☐ First 1:1 with a new
   team member

☐ Goal-setting meeting

☐ Performance review
   debrief

☐ Performance
   improvement meeting

☐ Skip-level meeting
   template

☐ Growth conversation

Agenda
(list of topics)
....
....
....
....
....

Meeting discusion notes

Observations / Concerns

Action Items

Follow up meeting plan

Notes

Meeting with

Date

1-2-1 type

☐ Regular check-in

☐ First 1:1 with a new team member

☐ Goal-setting meeting

☐ Performance review debrief

☐ Performance improvement meeting

☐ Skip-level meeting template

☐ Growth conversation

Agenda
(list of topics)

Meeting discusion notes

Observations / Concerns

Action Items

Follow up meeting plan

Notes

Meeting with

Date

1-2-1 type

☐ Regular check-in

☐ First 1:1 with a new team member

☐ Goal-setting meeting

☐ Performance review debrief

☐ Performance improvement meeting

☐ Skip-level meeting template

☐ Growth conversation

Agenda
(list of topics)

Meeting discusion notes

90

Observations / Concerns

Action Items

Follow up meeting plan

Notes

Meeting with

Date

1-2-1 type

- [ ] Regular check-in
- [ ] First 1:1 with a new team member
- [ ] Goal-setting meeting
- [ ] Performance review debrief
- [ ] Performance improvement meeting
- [ ] Skip-level meeting template
- [ ] Growth conversation

Agenda
(list of topics)

Meeting discusion notes

Observations / Concerns

Action Items

Follow up meeting plan

Notes

Meeting with

Date

1-2-1 type

☐ Regular check-in

☐ First 1:1 with a new team member

☐ Goal-setting meeting

☐ Performance review debrief

☐ Performance improvement meeting

☐ Skip-level meeting template

☐ Growth conversation

Agenda
(list of topics)

Meeting discusion notes

Observations / Concerns

Action Items

Follow up meeting plan

Notes

Meeting with

Date

1-2-1 type
- [ ] Regular check-in
- [ ] First 1:1 with a new team member
- [ ] Goal-setting meeting
- [ ] Performance review debrief
- [ ] Performance improvement meeting
- [ ] Skip-level meeting template
- [ ] Growth conversation

Agenda
(list of topics)

Meeting discusion notes

Observations / Concerns

Action Items

Follow up meeting plan

Notes

Meeting with

Date

1-2-1 type
- [ ] Regular check-in
- [ ] First 1:1 with a new team member
- [ ] Goal-setting meeting
- [ ] Performance review debrief
- [ ] Performance improvement meeting
- [ ] Skip-level meeting template
- [ ] Growth conversation

Agenda
(list of topics)

Meeting discusion notes

Observations / Concerns

Action Items

Follow up meeting plan

Notes

Meeting with
....
....

Date

1-2-1 type
- ☐ Regular check-in
- ☐ First 1:1 with a new team member
- ☐ Goal-setting meeting
- ☐ Performance review debrief
- ☐ Performance improvement meeting
- ☐ Skip-level meeting template
- ☐ Growth conversation

Agenda
(list of topics)
....
....
....
....
....

Meeting discusion notes
....
....
....
....
....
....
....
....
....
....
....
....
....
....
....
....
....
....
....
....
....
....
....
....
....

Made in United States
North Haven, CT
30 June 2022